WEIRD AND WONDERFUL
WEAPONRY

Published 1975 by Enterprise Books
Secausus, New Jersey

Copyright © 1975 by Intercontinental Book Productions
Library of Congress Catalog Card Number 74–24830

ISBN 0–89009–033–5

Printed and bound in Belgium

WEIRD AND WONDERFUL
WEAPONRY

Written by Major Eric N. Hebden
Illustrated by Michael Strand
Cover illustration by Brian Edwards

ENTERPRISE BOOKS

Contents

Cannons, Guns and Mortars   6
Hand Guns   12
Pistols and Revolvers   16
Multi-Fire and Machine Guns   22
Slings and Projectors   26
Rockets   30
Edged Weapons   34
War Machines   38

Introduction

The first man fought literally 'tooth and nail,' biting and clawing to defend himself or to kill animals for food. As his intelligence increased, so did his means of attack and defence. He began with a simple wooden club, which was developed by attaching a stone head to it, and by the period 10,000 BC he had learned to chip flints, giving a sharp edge to his hafted club or axe.

From there it was but a step to spears and, when he had learned to make a bow, flint-tipped arrows, which gave him a long-distance weapon.

And so, from these simple beginnings, man has progressed into the nuclear-exterminating age, inventing on the way many strange and bizarre weapons and war machines.

The dictionary defines 'bizarre' as 'odd, fantastic and whimsical,' and it must be said that the bizarre aspect is in the eye of the beholder. War machines quite familiar to us, like the tank, would have appeared fantastic to the ancient warrior, and equally many of his warlike products look odd and whimsical to us today.

And so it is in modern times. Sophisticated and complicated weapons may not look remarkable to the men who use them. But to the man-in-the-street they are bizarre objects . . . and expensive ones at that.

Cannons Guns & Mortars

The Pot de Feur

One of the earliest forms of cannon, this 'pot' is illustrated in a 1326 manuscript at Christ College, Oxford in England. It fired brass arrows.

An early type of cannon was mounted on a frame, allowing adjustments to be made to the angle of sight. The missiles were stones, the powder being ignited by a hot iron or live coal.

The original inventor of gunpowder is unknown. It was certainly used in China and India long before it was known in Europe, but Roger Bacon, the English friar, discovered its properties in 1242 AD, making it up into children's fireworks.

It is claimed that a German monk, Bethold Schwartz, living in Flanders, made the first cannon using gunpowder as a propellant in 1313 AD. He called it a Vari, or Pot de Feur.

Ammunition for cannon was various, ranging from iron arrows through stone-shot to iron cannon-balls, and in Germany mortars were filled with walnut-sized pebbles — the first form of grapeshot.

Later technical advances improved weapons and ammunition, the development of the gun making steady progress, particularly during times of war. However, the peak for the gun was probably reached during and shortly after, the Second World War. Now, though still of some importance as a weapon, the gun is on the decline. Tanks still carry them, but the heavier calibers are disappearing (coastal artillery is obsolete), and the time is not far away when guns and mortars will have been superseded entirely by rocket-powered high-explosive or nuclear-headed missiles. Meanwhile, some of the more bizarre-looking weapons using gunpowder are shown on these pages.

Early Cannon

In most books on cannon and guns the 'Pot de Feur' is illustrated, for it is the earliest known representation of a cannon. Incorporated in it is the basic principle of a metal container, with a gunpowder charge inside it, firing a missile. Some later guns, particularly in the East, were made of wood or leather. Wooden guns were still being fired from the Taku Forts near Peking in 1861.

The 'depression gun' shows the need which existed for a weapon which could fire down from the height of

The Bombard

Depression Cannon

defended walls on to the attackers below. Some form of wad would have been required to prevent the ball or missile rolling out before the cannon could be fired.

Cannon Bombard

Bombards, or, as we call them, mortars, were first used by the Italians. The object was to hurl the missile, usually a stone ball, over the castle or town wall being attacked, so destroying the buildings within it.

A mortar-like cannon in use in the Middle Ages in Europe. This type was widely used in sieges.

This small cannon, mounted on an adjustable wooden frame, was excellent for defending castle walls as its muzzle could be depressed to fire downwards.

A form of mortar from the early 15th century. This one can be seen in the Heeresgeschichtliches Museum, Vienna. It weighs nearly 8 tons, has a caliber of 35·2 inches, and the barrel is 8 feet 3 inches in length.

Giant Perrier

'Mons Meg'

A giant cannon still to be seen at Edinburgh Castle. The barrel consists of iron bars, bound by iron rings. It is said to have been presented to King James II of Scotland in 1451 by Molise McKim, a smith of Thriew. He was rewarded with the estate of Mollance, pronounced 'Mowans.' The gun was named after his loud-voiced wife, Meg, being first 'Mowans Meg,' then 'Mons Meg.'

An Austrian hand cannon of c. 1505. It came from the arsenal of Maximilian I.

In contrast to the Giant Perrier, this Austrian gun of 1635 has a caliber of only 1·4 inches, though the barrel is 8 feet long.

A later development of this idea was used during the great Siege of Gibraltar in 1783. The Spanish and French, after immense effort, sailed a fleet of floating wooden gun platforms across Algeciras Bay in order to get close enough to the Rock to try to bombard it into surrender. In return, 'depression guns' fired red-hot cannon balls (heated in braziers) down on the advancing floats. Foreseeing this danger, the invaders had protected their batteries with shields fixed overhead. And as an added precaution these were kept constantly wet with sea water. Yet the pounding cannon-fire from the Rock

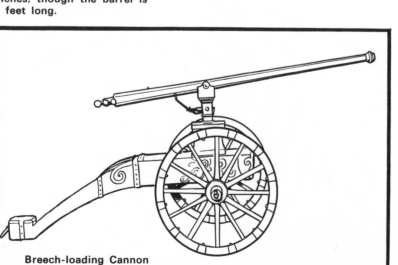

Breech-loading Cannon

Austrian Hand Cannon

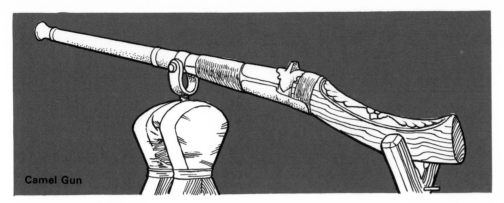

Camel Gun

An 18th century gun mounted on a wooden saddle for firing from a camel's back.

An American invention of 1862 for means of defence against surprise attack when working in the fields. The plow share served to anchor it firmly to the ground when firing.

This 24-pounder was invented by Lieut. Koehler during the siege of Gibraltar in 1783. The gun fired red-hot shot downwards at the besieging Spanish ships in the Bay. It had wet wads of paper between the powder charge and the hot cannon-ball, and more wads stuffed down the barrel prevented the shot rolling out before being fired.

An 18th century bronze mortar, believed to have been made for Tipu Sahib of Seringapatam in India. He had a fixation about tigers, and two of his tiger-muzzled guns can be seen at the Royal Military Academy, Sandhurst, England.

took its toll. The floating gun platforms were destroyed and the siege collapsed.

Many guns were made with the muzzles representing the wide-open mouth of a savage animal, but Tipu Sahib's 'tiger gun' is rare in that it is fashioned in the whole form of an animal.

The need for anti-aircraft guns came with the arrival of military airships and balloons, which were normally field pieces adapted to the purpose.

The French 11-pounder of 1910 was mobilized by mounting it on a 50-hp car, making it one of the earliest types of mobile A.A. guns. The number of times it actually hit an airborne target is not recorded.

French & Fancher.
Plow.
Nº 36,600.   *Patented Jun. 17, 1862.*

Fig 1

Fig 2

Witnesses:
R. F. Osgood
D. C. Johnson

The Plow Gun

Inventors:
C. W. French
W. W. Fancher
by S. Cross his atty.

The Red-hot Shot Gun

War, as usual, produced many and varied guns, the artillery of the First World War being one of the strongest arms, as bombing from the air was still in its infancy and was largely ineffective. However, the famous 'Paris Gun,' which bombarded the French capital city in 1918, had more of a psychological effect than a damaging one, as its shells were relatively light in weight and explosive content.

Guns big in weight and caliber could be based on concrete emplace-

Tiger Gun

The Wind Cannon

ments, as in coastal artillery; but mobility was a different matter. Special gun carriages on railways were used in both world wars, and during the Second World War huge vehicles were designed to take the weight of the heaviest field guns. The American 'Little David' mortar is a good example of this.

The 'wind machine,' one of Germany's secret weapons in 1945, did not come into operation before the end of the war, though the principle of using high-speed jets of air against low-flying aircraft might be said to have been a sound one.

One of many desperate ideas produced by the Germans at the end of the Second World War, when petrol and planes were in short supply. The wind cannon was conceived in a Stuttgart factory. It was intended to expel a high-speed jet of air at aerial targets, but it was never used in action.

A French 11-pounder gun of 1910, mounted on an automobile, for attacking enemy balloons and airships. It was elevated by a toothed arc. The rear wheels of the car were raised by jacks to take the strain.

Balloon Gun

'The Observer Gun'

No one was more prolific in designing odd and bizarre weapons than Britain's W. Heath Robinson. His unique drawings were featured in the *Sphere* and *Illustrated London News,* and were collected into a book titled 'Some Frightful War Pictures' in 1915. This was his suggestion for observing the enemy at a distance!

The Paris Gun

A German gun which bombarded Paris from over 67 miles away in 1918. An inner tube was inserted into a naval 15-inch gun, reducing the caliber to 8·26 inches. The shell reached an altitude of 24 miles. The struts kept the barrel perfectly straight.

An American 914-mm mortar used against subterranean fortifications and fortified cities during the Second World War. It was completed just before VJ Day. It fired a projectile of 3,700 lb with 1,600 lb of high explosive. The small picture next to the one below, shows 'Little David' in action.

'Little David'

Hand Guns

Matchlock Buckler

Hand guns are first mentioned being used in Europe at the Siege of Arras in 1414 and they were in general use by 1446. There is no doubt, however, that they were in action in the Middle and Far East many years earlier than this.

The earliest hand gun was fired by means of a slow-match or tinder-stick. Then came the matchlock, a simple device fitted to the side of the piece, one end forming the trigger, the other holding the match which could be swivelled on to the firing pan.

The flintlock was an improvement, a piece of flint being held in the cock-jaws, which produced a spark when spring-released to strike a flat piece of steel.

Armament popular in England in the 16th century. A wooden shield faced with steel plates had a pistol or short carbine protruding from the center. Ignition was by slow-match — a slowly-burning fuse made of chemically-impregnated rope.

A simple iron or brass tube with a touch-hole on top, the tube fixed to a straight stock of wood. For use on horseback, it was attached to the breastplate and a forked rest served to steady it.

Early Hand Gun

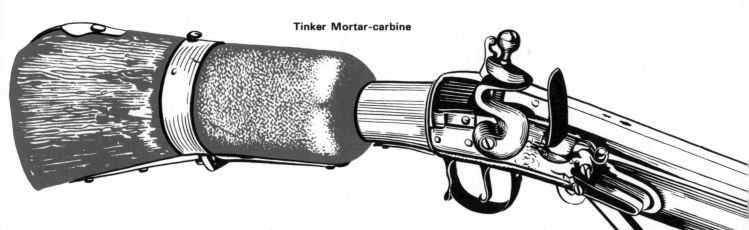

Tinker Mortar-carbine

Arrow-firing Musket

Invented by John Tinker in 1681. The wooden butt is hinged and can be withdrawn from the metal cup of the mortar. When closed, the weapon reverts to its normal role of carbine.

An illustration in Thomas Smith's 'Additions to the Book of Gunnery,' dated 1643. It portrays a musketeer firing off an incendiary arrow.

An Italian flintlock carbine of c. 1690, fitted with a war hammer for close-quarter work. There are many examples of guns being fitted with axe-heads.

An Italian weapon of c.1520. It combined a steel wheel-lock gun with a steel cross-bow.

Next came percussion caps and finally the breech-loading rifle with the percussion cap contained in the end of the cartridge which held the charge and bullet.

Many variations of designs, some of a bizarre nature, have been produced, and not only gunpowder, but springs, compressed air and gases have been used in hand guns to eject the ball or bullet from the barrel.

Hand guns were not confined to gunpowder as a propellant charge. Air-guns could be said to date from the days of the blow-pipe, a weapon still existing in some parts of the world. A further refinement of the air-gun came with the introduction of the pumped-up air-gun, in which a charge of compressed air for each shot was taken from a

Hammer-gun

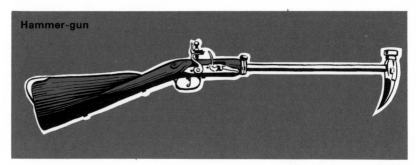

Gun and Crossbow

Pistol with Detachable Butt

Hand Mortar

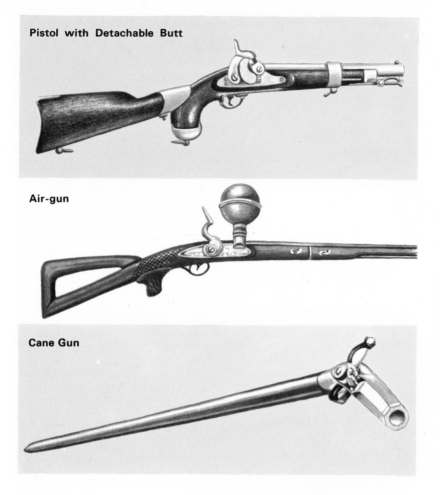

Air-gun

Cane Gun

An early form of hand-weapon on to which could be fitted a detachable butt, enabling it to be fired from the shoulder. This practice was common later.

An English sporting gun of 1778; on top is a cylinder of compressed air which expelled the bullet. These guns had the advantage of silence in action, but carried the threat of the cylinder exploding in the face of the sportsman.

A walking cane, c. 1814, concealing a flintlock gun which was quickly released when a spring was pressed. The concealed folding trigger came out when the gun was withdrawn and the hammer cocked.

A flintlock hand mortar made in Germany about 1740. It had a bronze barrel and would fire a small mortar-bomb over a wall.

reservoir, the air being previously pumped up to the correct pressure with a hand pump. The air reservoir was placed around the barrel, or in a butt container; alternatively, as in the example shown, it could be housed in a metal sphere screwed on to the barrel.

Guns or pistols concealed in apparently innocent-looking articles, such as a walking cane, were common enough in the last century and were well advertized by the makers. They no longer seem to be in fashion.

One of the more remarkable weapons used during the Second World War was the 'Krummlauf,' the German machine-pistol adapted for firing around corners, so giving maximum protection to the firer. It was in action during the street fighting in Russia. Some Americans developed a similar weapon later, fitting a curved barrel attachment to the M3 machine-pistol. It was fired not unsuccessfully during the Korean War. It is known that some Russian infantrymen are armed with around-the-corner weapons nowadays.

The idea was not new and had been tried out during the 19th century with flintlock hand guns.

'Around-the-corner' Gun

15

Pistols & Revolvers

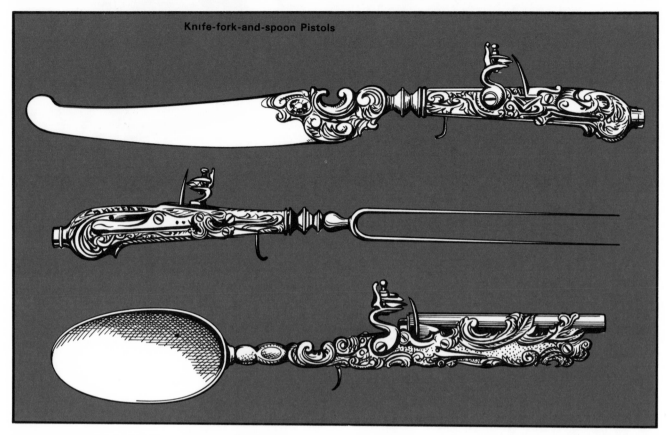

Knife-fork-and-spoon Pistols

A beautiful set of bronze-gilt tableware made in Germany in 1715. The pistols were exposed on top of the implements and had flintlock actions.

The small hand gun known as a pistol or revolver has for long been a favorite weapon because of its size and convenience. It is a comparatively light object, easy to carry, not difficult to hide or disguise, and though its range and accuracy may not be of the same standard as the musket or rifle, it was always a useful weapon at close quarters.

Its size lent itself to many bizarre designs, mainly directed to the purpose of disguising the gun. From knives and forks to a German-like *pickelhaube* helmet, all sorts of things have been brought into use to mount and conceal small pistols or automatics.

It could also be combined with another, usually bladed, weapon, though a whip pistol is shown, with the gun concealed in the handle. The Neapolitan bandit who wielded this amalgamation was doubtless no tyro with the whip.

Pistols, too, were useful in more violent times as protection for the innocent against common assault. In some models the butt could be swiftly adapted into a metal knuckle-duster if the first shot failed to find its target.

Americans have long been prolific inventors of odd hand guns, and arms catalogues in the last century and early in this one were full of ingenious

Spanish Key Pistol

An early Spanish example of a small flintlock pistol hidden in the end of a key. The barrel was the stem and pin of the key.

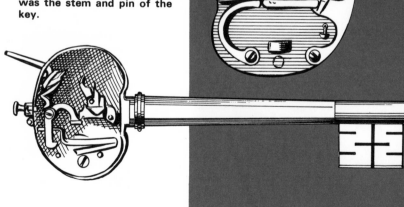

Whip Pistol

The Derringer

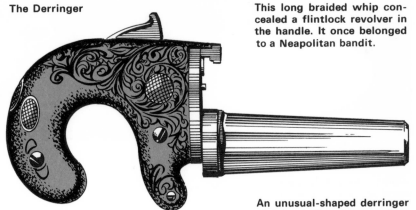

devices. Miniature guns for ladies' purses and lemon-squeezer pistols for assassins made their appearance regularly in the gunsmiths' pages — though the assassination sales-line was never mentioned, of course. It was assumed that weapons were bought for defence, never for offence.

The squeezer pistols, sometimes known as palm guns, were seldom bigger than a large pocket-watch — and, indeed, could be carried in a watch pocket. The firing action on the trigger was not in the conventional manner by the forefinger, but by the heel of the palm, the short barrel protruding through the fingers of the partly closed hand.

This long braided whip concealed a flintlock revolver in the handle. It once belonged to a Neapolitan bandit.

An unusual-shaped derringer pistol of American design, c. 1861. It fired cartridges and could be reversed in the hand to use as a striking weapon, using the ring-butt.

'The Pepperbox'

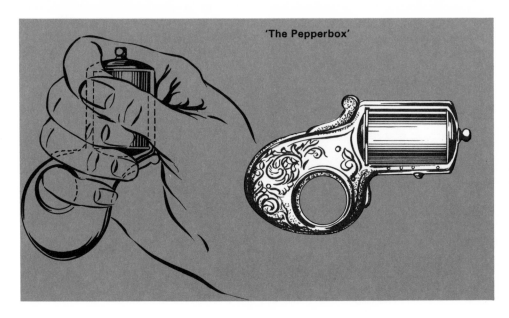

A short four-barrelled pistol invented by a Mr. Reid of New York in 1865. When the barrels were held in the fist, the ring-butt acted as a knuckle-duster.

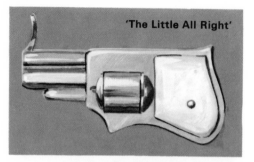

'The Apache'

'The Little All Right'

Cigar-case Pistol

A six-shot revolver with a built-in dagger. The hinged butt served as a knuckle-duster. Made in France, c. 1880.

An odd squeezer pistol of 1876. When rested in the palm of the hand, the fore-finger rested on the trigger at the end of the barrel, pull-ing it towards the palm when firing. The American inventor christened it 'The Little All Right.'

Another type of squeezer pistol, small enough to fit inside a cigar-case for dis-guise. It is a French late 19th century Gaulois, 5-shot, 8-mm, only ⅝ inch thick.

A small palm pistol to be hidden in the hand. The car-tridges were loaded in the center cylinder. The barrel jutted out between the fin-gers and it was fired by press-ing the trigger with the palm of the hand. Favored for assassinations. American, c. 1890.

Some models had oval metal guards over the top and bottom of the barrel, enabling them to be used as striking weapons if necessary.

Miniature guns which could be carried in containers shaped like cigar-cases or hollowed-out pocket books were skilfully designed and manu-factured and would provoke no suspi-cion when innocently produced in tense situations.

Weapons concealed in walking sticks and canes have been common enough, but the sedate businessman with the carefully rolled umbrella would not be thought to be hiding a gun in his umbrella handle. At least, not until he had used it.

Fountain pens and pocket flashlights have also been containers for other more lethal objects. The advantage of the flashlight gun was that the bullet travelled along the center of the line of

'The Lemon-squeezer'

Knife-pistol

light, making aiming all that much easier. Simply illuminate the target — and press the trigger.

A briar pipe seems to be the unlikeliest container of all in which to carry a gun, but more than one kind of pipe disguise was used, some being all metal, though painted to look like wood. The pipe would need to be removed from the mouth before firing.

An automatic concealed inside a metal helmet shaped like a First World War German *pickelhaube* is odd indeed, particularly the method of firing it. The idea was that one simply turned towards the enemy and blew down a flexible tube, which presumably hung free when not in use. The man who thought up this one was quick to point out that the helmet could be used

19th century two-side-by-side ·36 caliber pistols with two hammers and two triggers for percussion cap ignition. The triggers and heavy dagger blade folded into the brass frame.

An odd ·22 cartridge pistol disguised as a briar pipe. The rifled barrel screwed into the bowl and the firing-pin was locked by pulling back a small button and turning it into a notch under the bowl. It was fired by pushing the button sideways out of the notch. American, 19th century.

Pipe-pistol

Flashlight Pistol

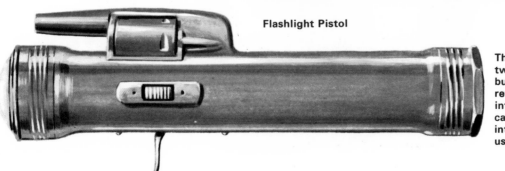

The flashlight was a normal two-cell type, with sliding button-switch. A 7-shot ·22 revolver unit was screwed into and on the front of the casing. The trigger folded into the casing when not in use. American, c. 1922.

The Watch Pistol

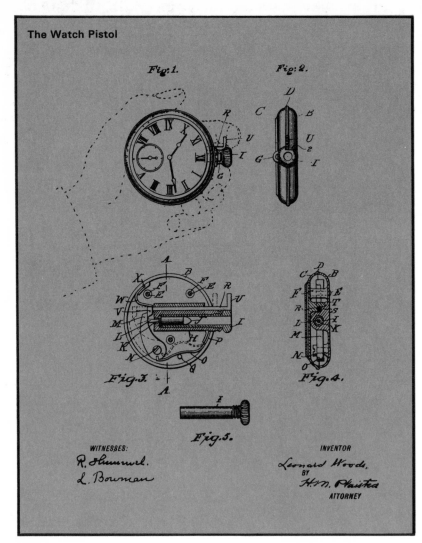

Fig:1. Fig:2.

Fig:3. Fig:4.

Fig:5.

WITNESSES:
R. Hummel.
L. Bowman.

INVENTOR
Leonard Woods,
BY
H.N. Plaistia
ATTORNEY

The Umbrella Pistol

The trigger was above the winder; when jerked back it manipulated the striker. American, c. 1913.

A 19th century French weapon, with a pepperbox pin-fire pistol hidden in the handle of the umbrella, until required for action.

An American Second World War 'fist gun,' for underground personnel. It was a single-shot pistol on the back of a glove. When the fist was closed, the trigger was exposed for contact. The weapon was fired by pressing or striking the fist against the adversary.

as a cooking utensil when not in more violent use. The spike could be stuck in the ground and the gun barrel used as a handle. It was patented but never found popular appeal.

The pistol concealed up the sleeve was far more practical. Imagine the surprise of an adversary who, having ordered his victim to 'stick 'em up,' found himself promptly shot in a most mysterious way.

The Nazi belt-buckle weapon was experimented with by the Germans but is not thought to have come into major production. The four barrels fired for-

Fist Pistol

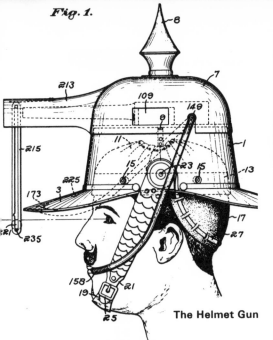

Fig. 1.

The Helmet Gun

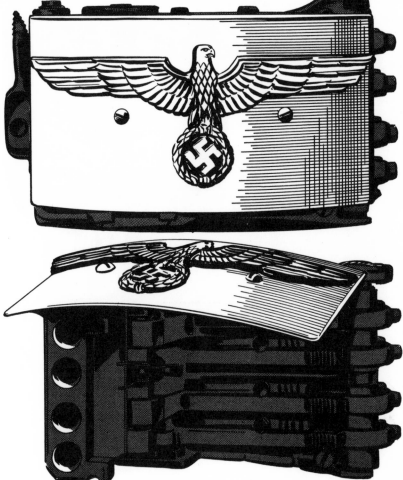

Nazi Belt-buckle Pistol

ward after the cover, with its swastika and eagle device, had been snapped up.

The 'fist gun' shown is one of several odd types manufactured during the Second World War, some being simple low-cost, stamped-metal, single-shot weapons dropped in quantity behind the German lines for use by the underground partisans. Others were more sophisticated. This one, mounted on a glove, had its trigger as an elongation of the barrel and needed to be pressed against the enemy's body to fire it. By this method it was difficult to miss.

Of all weapons and war machines, pistols and revolvers provide by far the biggest variety of odd and bizarre types.

A German Nazi 'secret weapon' of the Second World War. It had four barrels and four triggers, normally hidden. Two outside levers were squeezed, releasing the barrels which forced open the case cover. The shots could be fired one, two, three or four at a time.

Sleeve Pistol

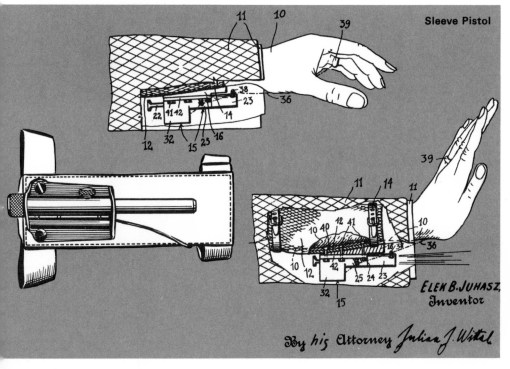

ELEK B. JUHASZ,
Inventor

By his Attorney Julian J. Wital

An American patent of 1916, combining an automatic revolver in a metal helmet. The gun was fired by blowing through the tube; this expanded a pneumatic bulb which acted as a trigger. The inventor also suggested that the helmet could be used as a cooking utensil.

A modern device of 1929 patented in America. The gun, on a leather mount, was fastened to the forearm with a rubber band. A wire from the striker ran to a ring on the finger, and when the hand was flipped up the gun fired. It used ·30 cartridges.

21

Multi-fire & Machine guns

Revolving Cannon

Seven cannon mounted on a revolving platform. An attempt in the Middle Ages to increase fire-power.

An early example of a multi-fire weapon, made in Germany. The five iron cannon were contained in a wooden jacket on a wooden carriage.

From the time that cannon and hand guns came into being, efforts were made to increase the fire-power of these new weapons. The most logical way in the earliest times was to mount several pieces together on one frame or carriage. This was done in various styles, some being quite ingenious.

The scythed chariot of pre-gun-powder days was improved by the addition of a contraption sometimes called a 'ribaudequin.' It might be termed the ancestor of the machine-gun.

A very early hand gun with multi-shot virtues was a form of mace with three or four metal barrels in the end of it. The ignition was simple, consisting of putting a slow-burning match or tinder to the powder in the touch-hole. They were known as 'Holy Water Sprinklers,' possibly because of a fancied resemblance to devices for doing just that. But another authority states, 'To sprinkle holy water was a cant phrase for fetching blood.'

Serpentine Cannon

'Over-and-under'

Multi-barrelled Gun

A German 'over-and-under' wheel-lock pistol of c. 1540. Although the locks were fitted to each side of the weapon, the barrels and triggers were above and below.

Multi-barreled weapons of the 17th century were called 'organs,' being cannon assembled together on one carriage and which could be fired off as one.

Wall guns, series of musket barrels on a wooden or metal frame, with a powder groove running the length of them at the rear, were also popular at this time in many countries. But the true machine-gun was still many years away and self-loading and self-cocking mechanisms would have to wait for the invention of the perfected metallic cartridge.

An early and unusual type of multi-barrelled gun, comprising a shaped board with a separate barrel at each corner. Of Austrian origin.

Six cannon mounted on a pike-bearing carriage. It had to be pushed into battle. French, c. 1550.

'Orgue des Bombardes'

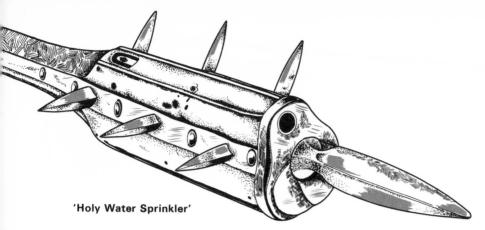

'Holy Water Sprinkler'

Known as the 'Holy Water Sprinkler,' this three barrelled gun at the end of a spiked mace had metal covers over the barrels not in action. English, c. 1547.

However, one form of a machine-gun was introduced surprisingly early when James Puckle, an Englishman, patented a weapon in 1718. At a trial carried out in 1722 it was said to have 'discharged sixty-three times in seven minutes by one man in the rain.' Puckle used two types of revolving blocks on a quite modern type of tripod. The blocks could hold seven or nine bullets,

round ones for Christians and square ones for Turks! A crank movement brought the chambers one by one to the breech and a half-turn made a tight grip. Each chamber had a flintlock attachment for firing. It was not taken up by the Government.

The 'Lillie' gun consisted of a wooden frame bearing two rows of rifled barrels, each row being fired by means of a crank which rotated the chambers, while cocking and releasing a hammer behind each barrel. There was a nipple screwed to the rear of each chamber, the loading consisting of inserting powder and ball into the chambers and placing a percussion cap on each nipple. Loading was cumbersome and it was not entirely successful.

The Billinghurst Requa gun had an interesting firing system. A sliding breech mechanism, operated by a lever,

Organ Gun

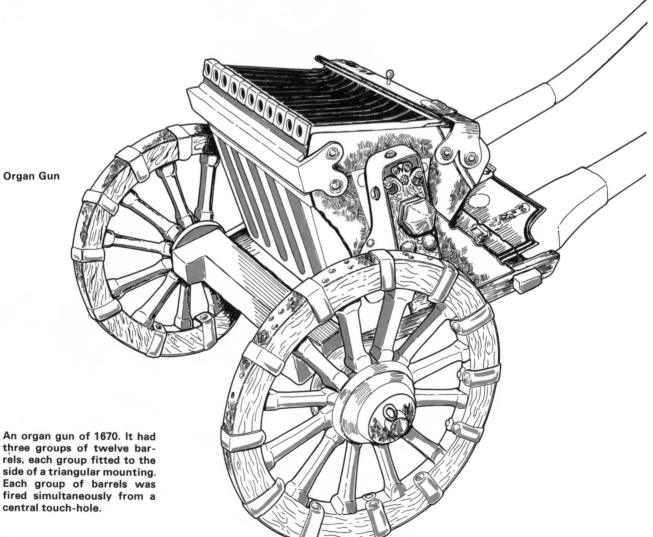

An organ gun of 1670. It had three groups of twelve barrels, each group fitted to the side of a triangular mounting. Each group of barrels was fired simultaneously from a central touch-hole.

'The Puckle Gun'

An early attempt at a machine-gun, this remarkable weapon was invented in 1718 by Englishman James Puckle. The gun was fired by a flint-lock mechanism.

A rapid-fire gun developed in America c. 1860 at the Billing-hurst Company of Rochester, N.Y., by Dr. Josephus Requa. The caliber of the 25 barrels was ·58 inches, and it was capable of firing 175 shots per minute.

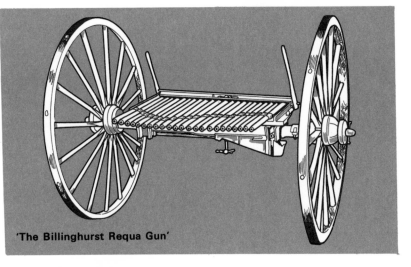

'The Billinghurst Requa Gun'

locked in the twenty-five cartridges, each perforated at the bottom. Each cartridge base was exposed to a chan-nel filled with priming powder; this was fired by a single hammer striking a percussion cap placed on a nipple.

The French 'mitrailleuse' with 37, later 25, rifle barrels could fire up to 444 rounds per minute. It was put to the wrong tactical use in the Franco-Prussian War and it was never used to the full extent of its power.

A successful French machine-gun used in the Franco-Prus-sian War of 1870–71. It had between 25 and 37 barrels, with a breech-plate holding the correct number of rounds. The plates could be changed 12 times per minute.

'The Mitrailleuse'

Slings & Projectors

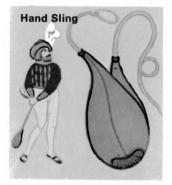

Hand Sling

An early personal weapon of leather and cords, for slinging stones or iron missiles.

The sling principle carried further. A Greco-Roman device for hurling missiles in pairs.

A simple pliant-armed catapult with sling for hurling stones, using twisted skeins of rope for tension.

The Springald

One of primitive man's first weapons was the sling, used for hurling stones. The principle of this was later developed into the siege machines used by the Greeks and Romans. These machines grew bigger and better in Norman times, and by the Middle Ages massive contraptions taking days and weeks to move and hours to prepare for action were used against besieged castles and towns.

These great engines of war, in their tactical deployment, were the equivalent of modern artillery. The catapulta, onager, trebuchet, and mangonel, with their high-dropping trajectory, were

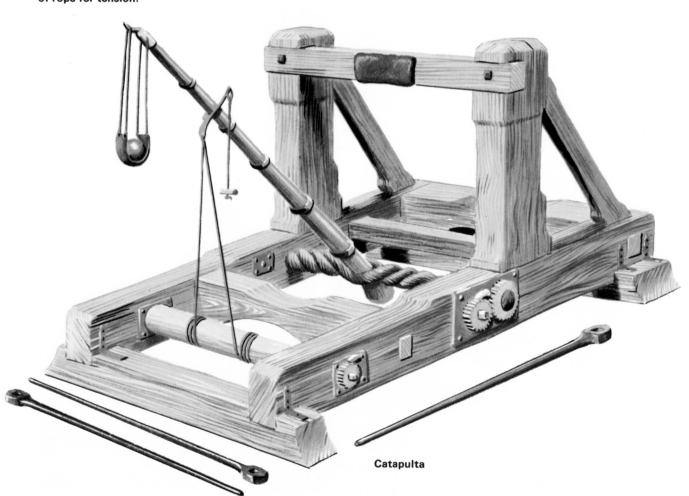

Catapulta

Short-armed Catapult

the howitzers of their time. The balista, firing on a flat trajectory, was the equivalent of our gun; and multi-missile projectors like the arcubalsta and the springald were, in effect, like early machine-guns.

The catapult came in two basic types, one having a sling at the end of the projecting arm, the other having a cup-shaped depression. The first type, used by the Greeks and Romans (the Greeks were the finest builders of these early war-machines) was lighter and the sling gave it a longer range.

To load and fire, the twisted cord was torsioned by the windlass. The missiles, usually stones, were then placed in the sling or cup. On operating the quick-release catch, the arm flew forward, coming into violent contact with the cross-beam, so discharging the missile.

The Onager

The Trebuchet

A short-armed catapult with cup at the end of the arm, allowing it to be used without a sling.

A form of catapult known as an 'onager,' or wild ass, which kicks stones up behind itself when running.

The trebuchet worked on the counter-weight principle, using the force of gravity for power rather than twisted cords or ropes.

27

The Disease-machine

The trebuchet worked on a different principle from the catapult, using the force of gravity for power. This was a huge machine which could have a most devastating effect, being capable of hurling a missile of 200 to 300 lb for a distance of 600 yards. Slings were always used to hold the projectile, and anything from stones to dead animals (to cause pestilence), or burning barrels of incendiary material (to cause fires), could be fired off. The trebuchet was made up of a base bearing two upright frames which housed the axle through the revolving arm. One end of the arm held the sling, the other the counterweight. There was a windlass for winching down the arm to the firing position.

The balista was simply a large crossbow fixed to a stand. A wooden pedestal carried a moveable top-carriage divided into three compartments, the outer two housing the twisted cords for propulsion, and each containing a short lever. The middle compartment supported the cradle which had a rack, block and winding gear. The block was wound back along the cradle, being held by a quick-release catch. The missiles — arrows, bolts or stones — were loaded in front of the block and the catch released.

The last picture here shows that someone had not forgotten his history lessons. A British officer during the First World War devised a spring-operated catapult for projecting hand-grenades against the enemy. Its operation was simple enough and its detachment of four men worked strictly to a drill . . . as might be expected.

Germ warfare is nothing new. In the Middle Ages they were using trebuchet to hurl putrefying carcasses of animals into besieged towns in order to spread disease.

Arcubalista

A more complicated form of balista, using two crossbows to discharge small stones or quarrels.

Balista

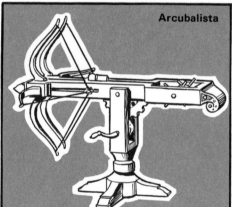

A huge crossbow fixed to a stand, the bow being placed under tension by a windlass and ratchet device. It fired metal-tipped arrows or bolts (iron darts with brass feathers).

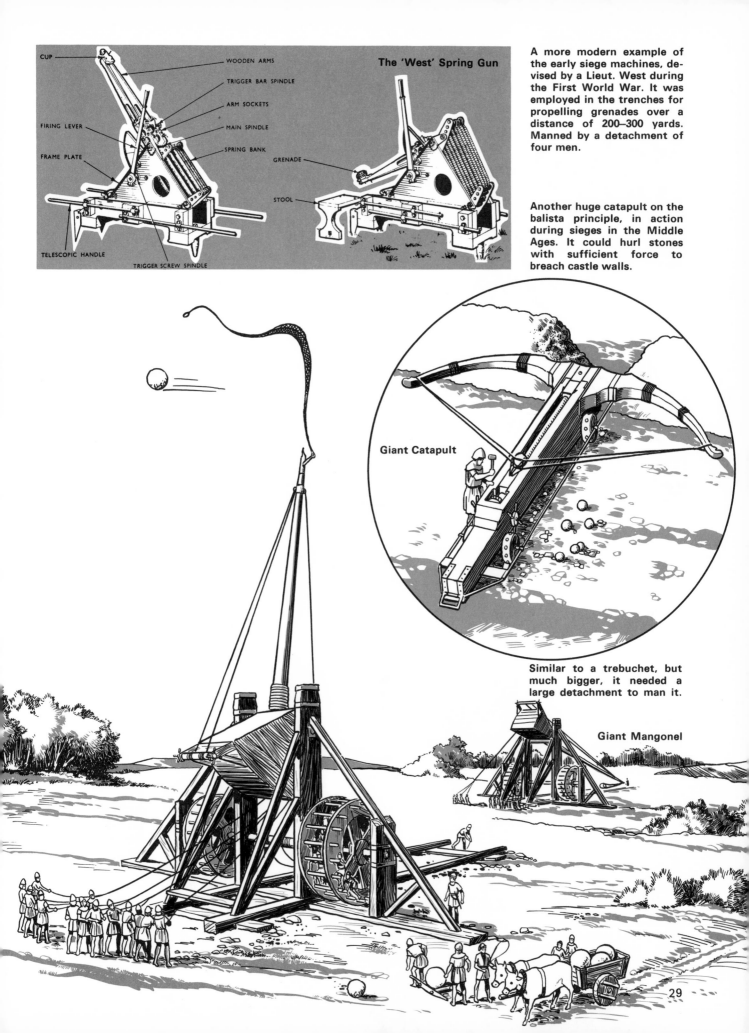

The 'West' Spring Gun

CUP
WOODEN ARMS
TRIGGER BAR SPINDLE
ARM SOCKETS
MAIN SPINDLE
FIRING LEVER
SPRING BANK
FRAME PLATE
GRENADE
TELESCOPIC HANDLE
STOOL
TRIGGER SCREW SPINDLE

A more modern example of the early siege machines, devised by a Lieut. West during the First World War. It was employed in the trenches for propelling grenades over a distance of 200–300 yards. Manned by a detachment of four men.

Another huge catapult on the balista principle, in action during sieges in the Middle Ages. It could hurl stones with sufficient force to breach castle walls.

Giant Catapult

Similar to a trebuchet, but much bigger, it needed a large detachment to man it.

Giant Mangonel

Rockets

Arab Land-rocket

The rocket was in use as a weapon before the invention of gun-powder, and there are many authorities showing its use by the Chinese, Arabs and Indians. The war rocket's use, however, declined during the 16th century when the science of artillery advanced. Guns had a longer range and were more reliable in operation. Also they could fire missiles which were both heavier and could be stored for longer periods. Rockets rapidly deteriorated.

In the 13th century, Hassan, an Arab writer, designed a rocket-propelled war vehicle made of two concave iron plates filled with an incendiary or explosive material. It was motivated by one or two rockets, with two long poles as guide sticks.

Mongolian Rocket-battery

This Mongolian rocket-battery of the 13th century, later developed by the Chinese, is the ancestor of the modern missile-launcher.

Two 15th century rocket-makers — the German Von Eichstadt and Joanes de Fontana, an Italian — both designed rocket-propelled wheeled vehicles filled with explosives, often in the shape of animals. Presumably to scare the enemy.

'The Hare'

However, rockets had a revival in the 18th century, particularly in India. Hydar Ali, the Ruler of Mysore, and his son Tipu Sahib used them with great effect against the army of the Hon. East India Company at Madras, and later at the Battle of Seringapatam, at which Colonel Wellesley, later the Duke of Wellington, was present.

Hydar Ali organised a corps of rocket-men, nearly 1,200 strong, armed with missiles similar to the European display rocket, but with iron casings and 10-foot bamboo guide sticks.

Colonel Sir William Congreve, a distinguished officer in the British Army, heard of the Indian war rockets and began experimenting with ordinary display sky rockets in 1801. By 1804 he had so improved the standard weak,

Rocket-torpedo

slow-burning mixture that he had a propulsive charge strong enough to send his rockets 2,000 yards.

The original Congreve pattern rocket was of incendiary type in a case of sheet-iron, 3 feet $4\frac{1}{2}$ inches long, $3\frac{1}{2}$ inches in diameter, with a guide stick 16 feet long.

Congreve's rockets were first used by the British Navy in 1805 and were later a feature of the Peninsular War of 1808–1814 – though Wellington thought little of them, preferring conventional artillery. Nevertheless, a Rocket Division was formed, armed with two carriages, 100 rockets and two reserve carriages. A new Rocket

Rocket-car

Fontana also designed a bizarre ram-rocket with a spike at the end. Possibly the first effort at making a naval torpedo.

A heavy rocket-driven wheeled car was another of Fontana's brain-children. And this was more feasible. It was designed to ram the gates of enemy-held towns or fortresses.

The Congreve Rocket System

In 1804 Colonel Congreve invented a war rocket in what became various weights and sizes, with different types of fillings. This picture shows his method of launching a 32-pounder rocket from a light ladder-like frame in the field. It would have been filled with 12 lb of powder and had a range of 2,000 yards.

The German 150-mm rocket
launcher named 'The Nebelwerfer' ('fog-thrower'), developed during the Second
World War, could discharge
six H.E. or smoke rockets to a
range of 7,330 yards, but
could fire only one at a time.

'The Nebelwerfer'

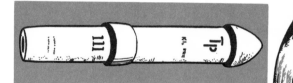

3-inch A.A. rockets were introduced by Britain in 1941.
A variation contained a 30-
inch towing parachute, 1,000
feet of wire cable, a small
round H.E. bomb, an 8-inch
drogue parachute, and a 46-
inch main parachute. It was
never entirely successful.

A.A. Rockets

Rocket Practice

The Congreve rocket system
survived until the middle of
the 19th century. This picture
is from an old print showing
the R.H.A. at rocket practice
at Woolwich in 1841.

Age had begun and Congreve became famous, rocketry spreading to many of the armies of Europe.

The British Army used rockets in most of the small wars of the 19th century, and they were in early use in the First World War. By 1916, the French were using them to bring down enemy balloons, firing the rockets from frames fitted to the struts of airplane wings. The French also mounted projector tubes on to automobiles and chased Zeppelins from below, firing off rockets at their airborne foes. The Germans used them to demolish barbed-wire defences, attaching small anchors to signal rockets. A line was attached to the stick, and when the anchor caught in the wire the line was winched in, bringing the wire with it.

The Second World War saw real progress in the military application of rocketry, though not all of the designs were entirely successful. The 'Z' batteries of Anti-Aircraft Command were sometimes more of a danger to their friends than their enemies, particularly when the A.A. rockets were fired before the launcher had been elevated.

The Germans were adept at the use of rocketry, but their V-1 and V-2 weapons perhaps came too late in the war to have the effect desired for them.

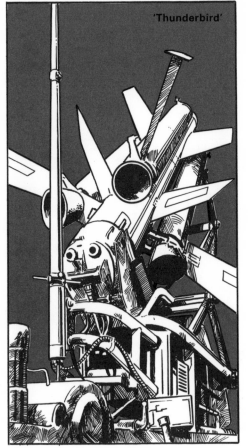

'Thunderbird'

A post-war rocket-missile weapon. This British 'Thunderbird 11' missile-launcher uses a radar guidance system for locating the target, then transmits a signal to the missile which locks on target.

A German development of the armored personnel carriers, Sd Kf.251, during the Second World War. Nearly 14 feet long, it was fitted with basket-like racks for launching six ground-to-ground rocket missiles.

Mobile Rocket Launcher

33

An early edged weapon mounted on a carriage for defending a breach made in a castle wall.

The Lyonors

Edged Weapons

The kukri, the Gurkha fighting knife, is well known, but there were stranger weapons in Nepal. In the Gurkha regiments today special kukris are used on feast days to kill a young animal as a sacrifice, but the true Nepalese sacrificial sword is the ram dao, which has a heavy, broad blade with a curved end, bearing an engraved or inlaid eye as a symbol.

To go West for a moment, the famous Bowie knife must be shown. The first one was made by an American blacksmith to the design of Colonel James Bowie, who commanded the Texas Army at the Alamo. Stories of his feats with the knife spread abroad and Bowie knives were soon being made in Europe, particularly in England, some with silver, horn or ivory grips.

The Moros natives of North Borneo made a powerful edged sword with a broad, leaf-shaped blade called a barong. The hilt had no guard and the carved, angled pommel is unusual.

To return to India again, we see the vicious types of hand-weapons made for in-fighting or assassinations. They fitted on the hand and bore sharp spikes like a tiger's claws. They were called bagh nakh. A variation was the bichwa, an effective double-ended dagger with the grip in the middle.

Executioner's Swords

These Indian decorated swords, with 30-inch blades 3 inches wide, were used for executions.

A variation of the standard katar, this Indian hand-weapon had a three-pronged blade, 8 inches long, possibly for piercing chain mail armor.

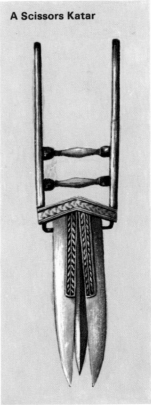

A Scissors Katar

An Indian dagger called a katar, with a 13½-inch blade, used for thrusting.

A Katar

The traditional weapon of Malaya, this wavy-bladed kris had a gold inlaid blade nearly 14 inches long.

A strange-looking weapon from Nepal. It is a sacrificial axe with a 31-inch blade, called a ram dao.

Made and used by the Moros tribe of North Borneo, a sword with a broad, leaf-blade and carved ivory pommel.

An oddly-shaped sword from Malabar, with a 27-inch sickle-shaped blade. Presumably for reaping heads.

This axe from India had a crescent-shaped head with a dagger screwed into the end of its copper-gilt shaft.

Queer-shaped blades abounded in the East, but the sickle-shaped blade of a sword from Malabar must be one of the oddest shapes for a personal weapon. Presumably the object was to reap enemy heads as one would reap corn.

European edged weapons such as swords, daggers, bayonets and halberds have been common enough for centuries, all following, more or less, the same conventional pattern. To look for the odder specimens, therefore, it is necessary to travel to the East, where local swordsmiths produced some remarkable weapons of bizarre designs. Highly decorated sword and dagger blades, hilts, pommels and scabbards were commonplace, particularly in India. The more formal the occasion, the more elaborate became the decoration, as on an executioner's sword.

The katar was an Indian dagger, an extension of the arm, for thrusting at

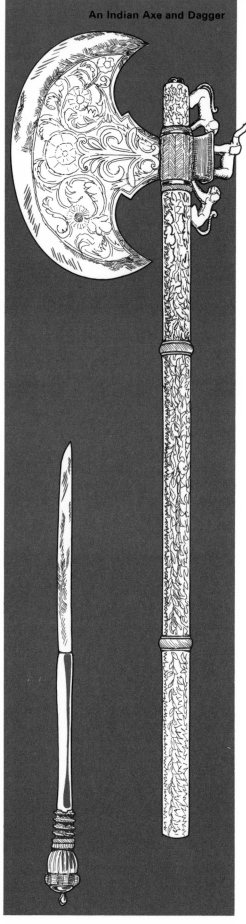

An Indian Axe and Dagger

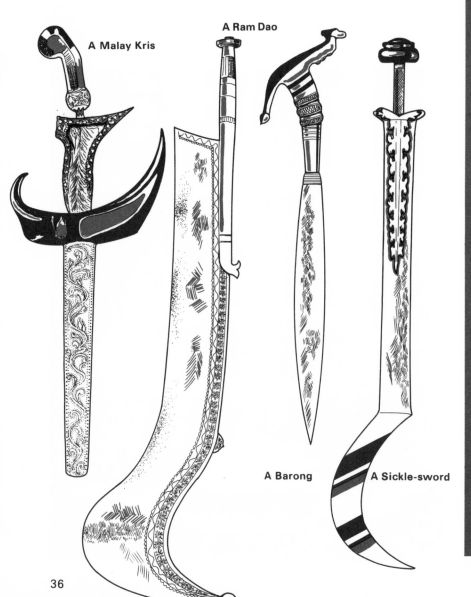

A Malay Kris

A Ram Dao

A Barong

A Sickle-sword

A Double-ended Dagger

Another Indian hand-weapon, called a bichwa, with double-ended blades, 7½ inches long.

the opponent. The hilt was formed of two parallel bars connected by two or more cross-bars. The tip of the blade was often reinforced for piercing chain mail armor. Variations of the katar had forked or serrated blades.

Some Eastern weapons are peculiar to their country of origin, like the Gurkha kukri of Nepal, the katana sword carried by the samurai of Japan, and the wavy-bladed kris of Malaya.

The kris had a finely-watered blade with a spiked tang on top which fitted into the hilt of wood or ivory, frequently beautifully carved.

Multi-weapons were not neglected, and in India the shaft of an axe would sometimes be used to hold a dagger, which screwed into the end of the shaft.

Designed by the famous Colonel James Bowie of the Texas Army, this British Victorian example had a pommel shaped like a horse's head and a 7½ inch blade.

Indian tiger's-claw weapons to fit on the hand, for in-fighting or, possibly, assassinations. They were called 'bagh nakh.'

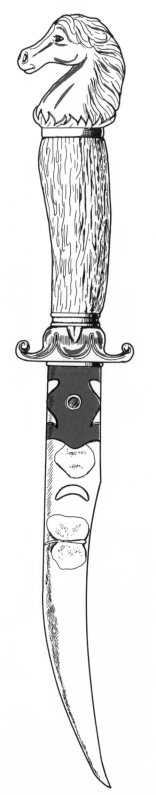

A Bowie Knife

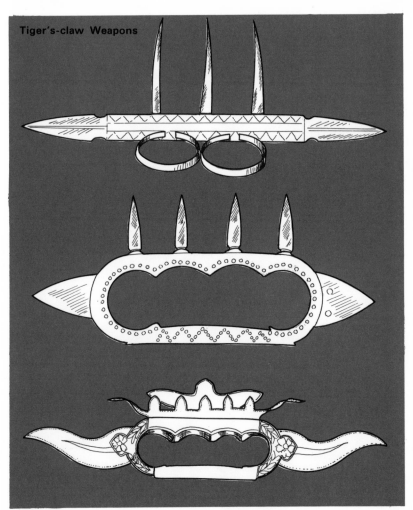

Tiger's-claw Weapons

War Machines

The Saxons and Angles from Germany destroyed many Roman-built walled towns in Britain with iron-headed battering rams.

The development of hand weapons from the club, through axe, spear and sword to the hand gun made it more and more imperative that the warrior should gain some personal protection from similar weapons in the hands of his enemy, and possibly the first 'war machine' was the knight in his suit of armor, astride a charger similarly encased.

Equally important was the need to invent machines and devices giving greater power and mobility to the army than could be provided by cavalry and infantry. It has therefore been the concern of rulers, governments and

Bolt-firer

Gear-operated Assault Bridge

An elaborate early European device for shooting bolts. The flexible arm was taken back under tension, then released to strike the head of the bolt fixed to an adjustable holder.

Another early type of war machine was this assault bridge, operated by a large gear wheel.

There is manuscript evidence to show that in the Middle Ages fire was carried into the enemy's ranks in pots lashed to a dog's back. The animal was given a scaled-metal coat and a long spike as an extra weapon.

fighting-men through the ages to acquire such devices, with the three main principles of power, mobility and protection in mind.

The object was achieved in our times with the invention of the modern armored-fighting vehicle, though present-day anti-tank weapons have made the 'protection' aspect wear thin at times.

In the Middle Ages mobility and power were gained in a primitive fashion by sending trained dogs in among the opposing forces carrying pots of fire on their backs — and some ancient manuscripts even show birds flying with pots of fire on their backs.

Fire-dog

'Armored Car'

Assault Bridge

Many attempts were made in the old days to safeguard soldiers during battle. This picture shows an early attempt at an 'armored car.'

The problem of breaching castle or town walls in the Middle Ages was often solved by elaborate mobile assault bridges, like the one depicted here.

An early design for a war machine of fantastic and frightening appearance. Called 'A fearsome engine of Arabia,' it fired pointed darts.

Designed by Leonardo da Vinci in 1500, this 'combat-vehicle' would allow eight men to propel themselves forward with hand-cranked transmission gear, at the same time remaining under the armored top.

(The first recorded instance of aerial warfare!) Much of the warfare in those times consisted of long, drawn-out sieges of castles and walled towns, so the production of siege machines, both for the attackers and the defenders, was prolific.

Great minds, like that of Leonardo da Vinci, were brought to bear on the subject of war machines, and it is said that da Vinci's notebook was full of sketches and designs for ingenious land-machines. One, a 'combat-vehicle,' is shown here. And it would have worked.

'The Fiery Dragon'

Combat-vehicle

A 15th century adaptation by John Zizka, a Bohemian Hussite, using four-wheeled, horse-drawn farm carts, making cannon mobile and at the same time giving protection to the gunners.

Battle-wagon

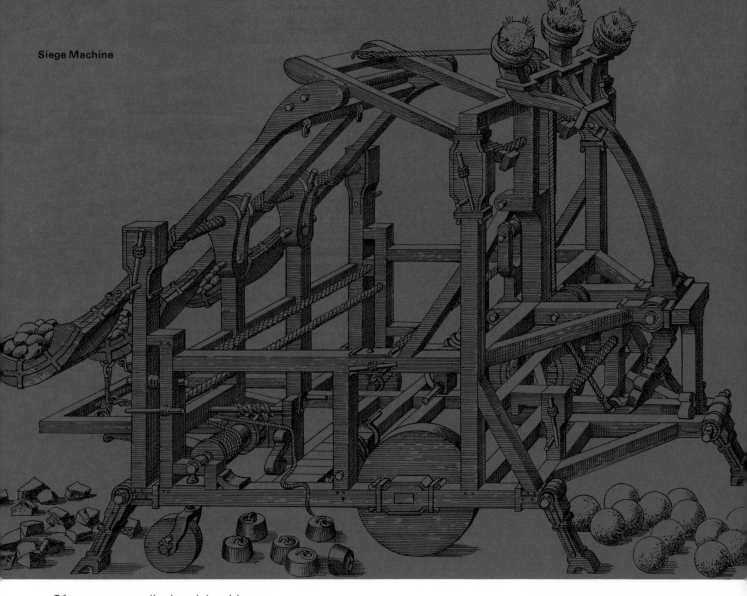

Of course not all pictorial evidence can be relied upon. 'The Fiery Dragon of Arabia' depicted in the 1483 edition of *Valturio* owes something to the artist's imagination — but certainly machines of awe-inspiring appearance, designed to frighten more than to kill, were common in Italy and Spain.

One of the remarkable aspects of early machines was the evidence of the superb craftsmanship which went into them, skill and ideas comparing favorably with modern technological know-how. The colossal siege machine may have something weird and wonderful about it, but it required men of stature and determination to design and make it.

The German war chariot shown would be used in land battles and is one type of many built on the same simple lines. Spears and tridents added their weight to the already heavily-laden cart, but these could come into action after the cannon had been

A colossal siege machine of c. 1588, designed to hurl stones and incendiary shells into the enemy stronghold.

A German war chariot, c. 1500, with four guns, probably falconets, protruding from the front of it.

War Chariot

41

Arcubalista

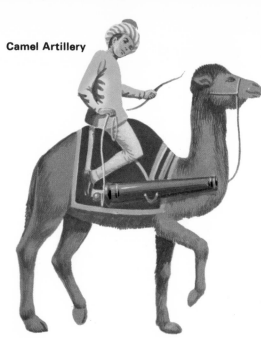

Camel Artillery

A powerful defensive machine of the late 16th century, capable of discharging round shot, heavy darts or incendiary shells at the attacking forces.

During the 18th century in the Ottoman Empire, muzzle-loading guns were carried on the sides of camels. The angle of sight was adjusted by a rope fastened to the pommel and the gun was fired by a long slow-match.

fired from a distance at the enemy ranks. One great drawback to this machine, or combat cart, was the need to remove the guns for reloading. They were, of course, muzzle-loaders.

Muzzle-loaders were not only carried on carts. In the Middle East the ubiquitous camel was employed as a gun-carrier and gun-platform; regardless of the success of the idea, the constant recoil of the fired gun, hanging down the camel's side, couldn't have done the poor beast much good.

By the 19th century, with the great advances in engineering techniques and the introduction of steam power, ideas for war machines flowed from the drawing boards, although not all of them were capable of working. But men were trying to get the better of

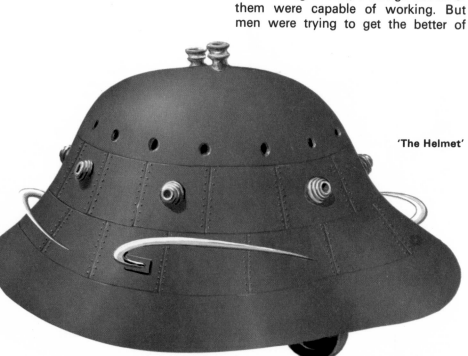

'The Helmet'

In the first half of the 19th century this helmet-shaped, steam-driven battle-wagon was designed by an Englishman, James Cowan. The Government considered it 'uncivilized' and refused to support it.

their neighbors — whether for national or pecuniary motives is not always clear — and to supply arms and machines to the armies of the world was big business, as it is today.

In the 20th century armor plate was being improved all the time, and the internal combustion engine gave a source of power and mobility not previously available. Battle wagons and armored cars began to appear in Europe, and the bright young inventors of America were not far behind.

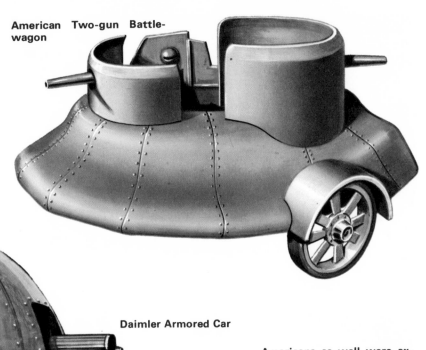

American Two-gun Battle-wagon

Daimler Armored Car

Americans as well were experimenting with mobile armored vehicles at the turn of the century, but this design got no further than the model stage.

The great engineering firm of Daimler produced this 3-ton armored car in 1906. It mounted only one machine-gun.

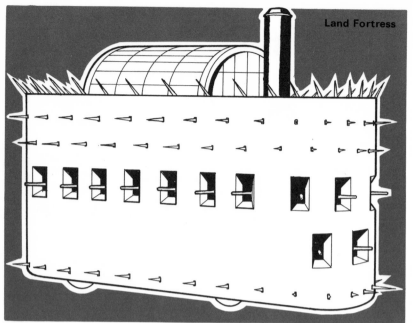

Land Fortress

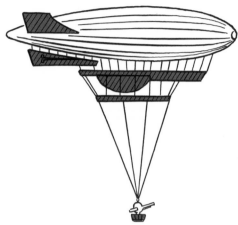

Airship Gun

German interest in battle-wagons was shown by this design of a land-fortress considered about 1900

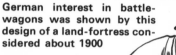

The Motor-cycle Gun

In 1899 a Mr. F. R. Simms demonstrated a Maxim-gun, mounted behind a shield on the front of a De Dion Bouton four-wheeled motor-cycle. There is no evidence that it was later taken into service.

Prior to the First World War the Germans in particular were experimenting with military airships. The picture above right, shows a design for suspending a field gun and detachment in a car slung beneath the airship.

In addition to its 20-hp engine, this Sizaire-Berwick armored car of 1915, the brainchild of the British Royal Naval Air Service, had a 110-hp aeroplane engine and propeller to assist its passage over soft desert sand, right.

Looming up in the near future was a war, the like of which the world had never seen before, and, as in all major conflicts, the stimulus given to the invention and building of war machines was tremendous . . . and regardless of cost.

In the years prior to the First World War military balloons and airships had made their appearance in the skies. Indeed, balloons had been used in the Franco-Prussian War of 1870. They were flown primarily as observation platforms, though later light armament was provided in the baskets and airship cars. A British officer's idea of slinging a field gun on a platform beneath an airship came to nothing, however: the problem of recoil could not be overcome.

The tank was a British invention, and the first slow-moving Mark 1, weighing 31 tons, armed with guns and machine-guns, went into action on the Western

'The Wind Wagon'

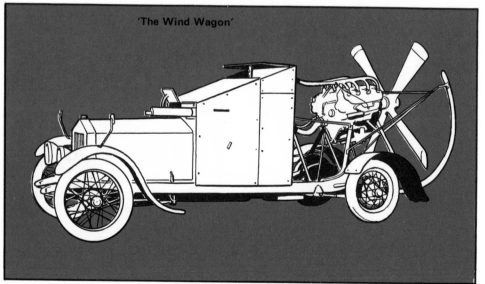

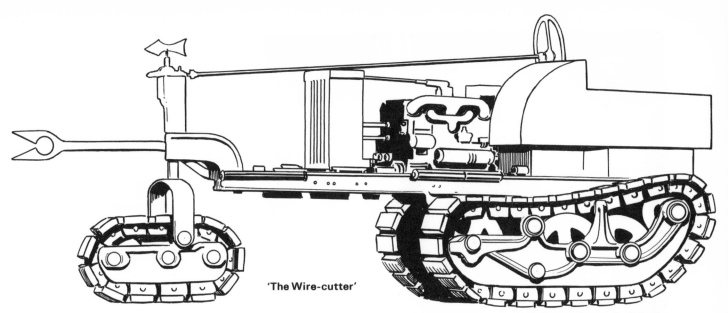

'The Wire-cutter'

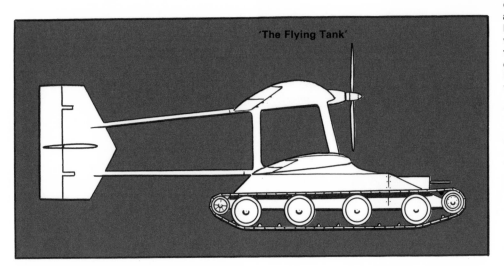

'The Flying Tank'

'Goliath'

A 1915 experiment in Britain of a tracked vehicle based on a triple-tracked American Killen-Strait tractor. Its object was to cross trenches and cut the wire entanglements. Its experimental use raised great hopes for tracked armored vehicles.

After the First World War many ideas were put forward for armored fighting vehicles, this being one of the more fanciful. Invented by Walter Christie for flying over obstacles, it had a 750-hp airplane engine and propeller. It could leap a 20-foot gap from a 45 degree ramp. Christie sold it to Russia.

A German midget tank of the Second World War, guided by remote control. Named 'Goliath,' it was only 26·3 inches high. It was filled with an explosive charge and used on blockhouses, road-blocks and minefields.

Front for the first time in February 1916. Unfortunately it was soon bogged down in the mud and mire, but its advent was startling enough to the Germans, who had failed to find an answer to it by the end of the war.

After the first premature launching, the tank was tried out again more successfully in better conditions and in greater strength in 1917 — and thereafter it became the most important war machine on land.

After the war, money became scarcer for developing war machines, particularly as it had been 'a war to end wars.' Some odd-looking machines were produced by private firms and individuals, however. Walter Christie's 'flying tank' was one example. After he had sold it to Russia, though, it disappeared into oblivion.

It was the men of Nazi Germany who first appreciated the power and strength of the tank arm, building improved

'The Bobbin'

beaches of France on D-Day would require something out of the ordinary, and they employed a remarkable officer named Major-General Hobart, a veteran tank man, to provide the answers. His 'funnies' of amphibious, mine-clearing, carpet-laying, bridge-building tanks added greatly to the success of the operation.

The Germans also had been bringing forth some unusual machines, their miniature 'Goliath' tank being one of them. Two methods of remote control were used; one payed out a three-string remote-control cable behind it to the control point, and the other worked by wireless control.

By the end of the war they were still trying to produce 'secret weapons,' but time was against them. It is noticeable too that they were building machines for attack and rarely for defence.

Tanks could get bogged down on beaches; this contrivance, fitted to a Churchill chassis, could lay a 10-foot wide canvas track on soft sand with the minimum of delay.

An amphibious conversion fitted to a Sherman tank. The canvas screen gave it buoyancy and it was driven at up to 4·3 knots by two propellers and its tracks.

A Sherman tank of the Second World War with a mine-clearing adaptation fitted to the front. It was capable of clearing a lane 10 feet wide.

models in increasing numbers after they came to power. They tried out their 'blitzkrieg' tactics in the Spanish Civil War of 1936, and again in 1940 when they swept through Poland, Holland, Belgium and France in but a few weeks.

The British and French had been slower off the mark and paid the price for it. Yet the resourcefulness and inventiveness of the British and, later, the Americans, eventually redressed the balance and some of the war machines employed in the Second World War were odd enough to be termed bizarre. Yet most of them worked.

The Allied planners realized that landing on the heavily-defended

'The Duplex Drive (D.D.)'

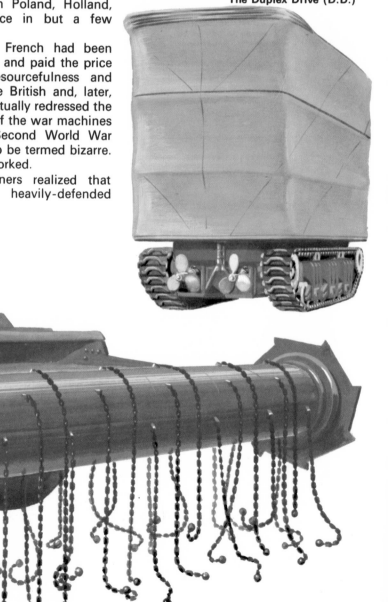

'The Crab'

INDEX TO ILLUSTRATIONS

A

A.A. Rockets 32
Air Gun 14
Airship Gun 44
Apache 18
Arab Land Rocket 30
Arcubalista 28, 42
Armored Car 39
Arrow-Firing Musket 13
Assault Bridge 39
Austrian Hand Cannon 8

B

Balista 28
Balloon Gun 10
Barong 36
Battle-wagon 40
Billinghurst Requa Gun 25
Belt-Buckle Pistol 21
'Bobbin' Tank 46
Bolt-firer 39
Bombard, the 7
Bowie Knife 37
Breech Loading Cannon 8

C

Camel Artillery 42
Camel Gun 9
Cane Gun 14
Cannon Bombard 7
Catapulta 26
Cigar-case Pistol 19
Combat-vehicle 40
Congreve Rocket System 31
'Crab' tank 46

D

Daimler Armored Car 43
Depression Cannon 7
Derringer 17
Disease Machine 28
Double-ended Dagger 37

'Duplex Drive' (D.D.) 46

E

Early Cannon 6
Early Hand Gun 12
Executioner's Sword 35

F

Fist Pistol 20
Fire-dog 39
Fiery Dragon 40
'Flying Tank' 45

G

Gear-operated Assault Bridge 39
Giant Catapult 29
Giant Mangonel 29
Giant Perrier 7
'Goliath' Tank 45
Gun and Crossbow 13

H

Hammer Gun 13
Hand Mortar 14
Hand Sling 26
'Hare' 30
'Helmet' Battle Wagon 42
Helmet Gun 21
Holy Water Sprinkler 24

I

Indian Axe 36
Indian Dagger 36

K

Katar 35
Knife-fork-and-spoon Pistols 16

Knife Pistol 19

L

Land Fortress 44
Lemon Squeezer 18
Little All Right 18
Little David 11
Lyonors 34

M

Malay Kris 36
Matchlock Buckler 12
Mitrailleuse 25
Mobile Rocket Launcher 33
Mongolian Rocket Battery 30
Mons Meg 8
Motor-cycle Gun 44
Multi-barrelled Gun 23

N

Nebelwerfer 32

O

Observer Gun 10
Onager 27
Organ Gun 24
Orgue des Bombardes 23
Over-and-under 23

P

Paris Gun 11
Pepperbox 17
Puckle Gun 25
Pipe Pistol 19
Pistol with Detachable Butt 14
Plow Gun 9
Pot-de-Feur 6

R

Ram Dao 36
Red Hot Shotgun 9
Revolving Cannon 22
Rocket Car 31
Rocket Practice 32
Rocket Torpedo 31
Around-the-Corner Gun 15

S

Saxon Battering-ram 38
Scissors Katar 35
Serpentine Cannon 22
Short-armed Catapult 27
Sickle Sword 36
Siege Machine 41
Sleeve Pistol 21
Spanish Key Pistol 16
Springald 26

T

'Thunderbird' 33
Tiger Gun 9
Tiger's Claw Weapons 37
Tinker Mortar-Carbine 13
Trebuchet 27
Two-gun Battle-wagon 43

U

Umbrella Pistol 20

W

War Chariot 41
Watch Pistol 20
'West' Spring Gun 29
Whip Pistol 17
Wind Cannon 10
'Wire Cutter' 45
'Wind-wagon' 44